NOT ONLY FOR DUCKS
THE STORY OF RAIN

TO PHILIP

who also has a great liking for looking

Published by Whittlesey House, a division of
the McGraw-Hill Book Company, Inc.
Printed in the United States of America

THE JUNIOR LITERARY GUILD AND
WHITTLESEY HOUSE
McGRAW-HILL BOOK COMPANY, INC.
New York   Toronto   London

NOT ONLY FOR DUCKS

The Story of Rain

by **GLENN O. BLOUGH,** SPECIALIST IN
ELEMENTARY SCIENCE, UNITED STATES OFFICE OF EDUCATION

pictures by **JEANNE BENDICK**

One day in early spring, Mrs. McBlossom was standing at the kitchen door of her farmhouse. She was watching the rain fall and thinking that it would soon be time to plant her garden.

"This rain is good for peppers and parsley and peas and parsnips," Mrs. McBlossom said to herself. "It is good for everything that grows."

Mrs. McBlossom was smiling. She always did when things pleased her.

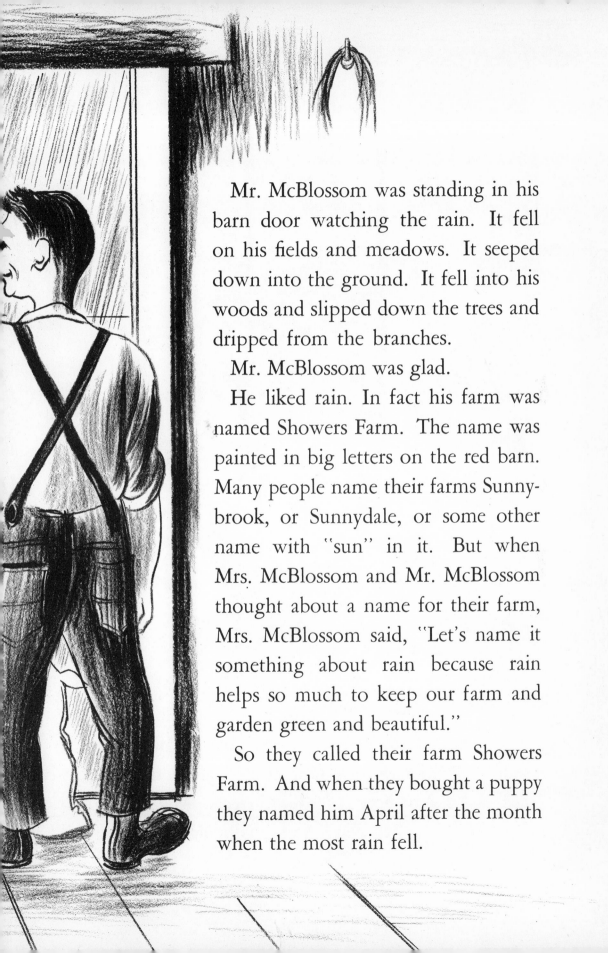

Mr. McBlossom was standing in his barn door watching the rain. It fell on his fields and meadows. It seeped down into the ground. It fell into his woods and slipped down the trees and dripped from the branches.

Mr. McBlossom was glad.

He liked rain. In fact his farm was named Showers Farm. The name was painted in big letters on the red barn. Many people name their farms Sunnybrook, or Sunnydale, or some other name with "sun" in it. But when Mrs. McBlossom and Mr. McBlossom thought about a name for their farm, Mrs. McBlossom said, "Let's name it something about rain because rain helps so much to keep our farm and garden green and beautiful."

So they called their farm Showers Farm. And when they bought a puppy they named him April after the month when the most rain fell.

Upstairs in his room young Mike McBlossom was watching the rain too. It splashed against the window and slid down the glass in little rivers. Mike was looking outdoors. He was watching the farm animals.

6

He saw the cows bunched up under a big tree in the meadow. They were standing quite still. Sometimes they switched their tails a little. He heard the chickens cackle and squawk and watched them run. Some ran under the hay wagon. Some ran into the henpen.

He heard the pigs grunt and squeal and saw them run into the pigpen. And there went the cat under the corncrib!

He watched the ducks. They just quacked among themselves, wiggled their tails, and looked for the wettest place around. They acted as if they thought that rain was a fine thing. If ducks could smile, they probably would when it rains.

But Mike was not smiling. He didn't even feel like it. He sat down on the floor of his room and began to work on his kite. It was a beautiful green kite and this was the day he had planned to fly it. But a rainy day is not a good day for flying kites.

Mike's dog April was lying on the floor beside him. April seemed to know that Mike was disappointed.

"April, this rain is a big nuisance," Mike said. "I wish the sun would shine and the wind would blow. Rain is only for ducks."

RAIN IN THE CITY

Down the lane from Showers Farm, up the road, past the church, and over the bridge was the city. In the city it was raining too! People looked down from their windows at the street below and saw the rain falling on the buses and the taxicabs. They saw it falling on people with umbrellas and on people without them.

In the city rain fell on everything out of doors and washed everything clean. It washed the buses and the taxicabs, and made them redder and bluer and yellower. It washed the streets and the sidewalks. The rain ran down the gutters and carried away all kinds of dirt that nobody likes to see. The rain in the city gave everything a bath, and everything needed it.

Rain came down from the sky and washed the dust and soot out of the air. Many people in the city said, "The rain is making the air smell good. It is making it fresh and clean." And it was.

Trees grew along the city streets. And in some places there was green grass. Rain fell on the trees and grass. That was a good thing. Trees and grass couldn't grow without rain in the city. They couldn't grow without rain on Showers Farm either.

Up in the mountains near the city, the rain fell on the slopes and ran down to the valley. There it was caught in a big reservoir. People in the city get their drinking water from this big reservoir. Like people in the country, people in the city use lots of water. They drink it. They wash themselves in it. They wash their clothes in it. They wash their cars in it. They use it in factories. It would take a long time to name all the things people in the city use water for.

Mike McBlossom liked to travel down the lane, up the road, past the church, and over the bridge to the city. He and his mother went to the city often to sell vegetables from the garden. Mr. McBlossom sold farm crops there too.

But Mike wasn't thinking of the city today. He just watched the rain and wished it would stop so that he could fly his kite.

RAIN IN THE COUNTRY

The rain fell down on the garden and fields and forest and meadows of Showers Farm. Rain always does that. That's because something called gravity pulls it down to the earth. Gravity is a pull that the earth has for everything on it and near it. Leaves fall down to the earth in autumn. Snow falls down. Apples fall. Balls fall. Gravity pulls them all.

Gravity even pulls on Mike McBlossom. It pulls 70 pounds on him. If you want to know how much gravity pulls on you, just weigh yourself. The scales will tell you.

Whenever the raindrops fell on the hillsides on Showers Farm, gravity pulled some of them together. They made a tiny trickle that ran down. More raindrops fell on the hillside. They made more trickles. These trickles ran together and made a tiny rill.

More rain fell and the rills joined each other and down the hill they went. More rain joined them and they made a tiny stream that hurried down the hillside to the valley. More rain fell and the trickles and rills and streams grew larger and joined to make quite a creek that ran down through the fields and meadows.

Cows drank water from the creek. Ducks quacked around it and swam in it. The creek was one of the merriest things on Showers Farm. It babbled and gurgled and slipped over stones and it sparkled when the sun shone on it. That is, it did all these things when there was enough rain.

DOWN HILLS

Mike McBlossom liked to play along the creek that ran through the meadow on the farm. Once he made a boat from a piece of bark. He filled it with acorns and put it in the water. Away it went down the creek. Gravity carried it down with the water. It bumped against the bank and spilled some of the acorns. Maybe they grew into oak trees on the bank of the river. Then it went on through the meadow until Mike couldn't see it.

It went under the bridge and past

PULLS WATER

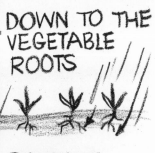

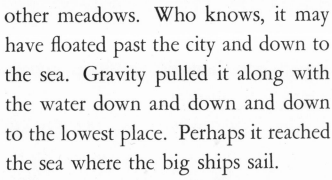

other meadows. Who knows, it may have floated past the city and down to the sea. Gravity pulled it along with the water down and down and down to the lowest place. Perhaps it reached the sea where the big ships sail.

But not all the raindrops that fell on Showers Farm ran downhill to form the creek. Some of them soaked into the ground of the farm. Gravity also pulls the water down into the ground. It pulls it down to the roots of the grass in the meadow.

It pulls it down farther to the roots of Mrs. McBlossom's peppers and parsley and peas and parsnips. Mrs. McBlossom likes that.

It pulls it down to the roots of the corn and clover in the fields. Mr. McBlossom likes that. If there is enough rain it soaks way down to the roots of the trees in the meadows and the woods. April likes that because he likes trees for chasing things up.

But sometimes when rain fell—like today—Mike wished that it wouldn't. He thought that rain was a nuisance, especially when he wanted to fly his kite.

RAIN IN THE SPRING

In spring on Showers Farm lots and lots of rain falls. It rains and then the sun shines and then it rains again. This is a good thing.

Showers Farm is a busy place in spring. Seeds can't plant themselves. Fields can't plow themselves. Everyone on the farm is busy planting and plowing and doing other things that need doing.

Even Mike is busy in spring because he plants his own garden. That's how he gets the vegetables he takes to sell in the city.

One day after a rain Mike was working in his garden. His mother was working in hers too. Mike was planting lima beans. "These beans look dead as a doornail," he said to his mother.

"Well, they're not," said Mrs. McBlossom. "Neither are these pepper seeds nor these parsley seeds nor these peas nor the parsnips. All they need is rain and a little time. You'll soon see that they are alive."

Mike McBlossom HAD A GREAT LIKING FOR LOOKING. He liked to look at all sorts of things. He looked at them so carefully that he sometimes discovered things that hardly anyone else knew. Because Mike HAD A GREAT LIKING FOR LOOKING his mother and father once gave him a large magnifying glass for Christmas. "This," they said, "will make little things look bigger and easier to see."

Mike looked at all sorts of things with his magnifying glass—at birds' feathers, at bees' stingers, at flies' eyes, at butterflies' feelers. He even looked for fleas on April.

It was Mike's habit of using his magnifying glass that made him think to look at his bean seeds a few days after he had planted them.

"My beans have been planted six days," he said to himself. "Guess I'll dig one up and take a look."

And he did.

MIKE LOOKED AT

BUTTERFLIES' FEELERS,

BIRDS' FEATHERS,

FLIES' EYES,

AND EVEN FLEAS

He dug down into the moist ground and found one of the seeds. It was all puffed up and the skin on the outside had cracked open. It felt moist. He took the skin off and opened the two halves of the bean. There inside he saw a very tiny thing. He looked at it with his magnifying glass. It looked bigger that way and he could see it better. It was a tiny bean plant.

THIS PART WAS GOING TO BE THE LEAVES

FOOD FOOD

THIS WAS GOING TO BE THE ROOT

One end of the plant was white and curled around like a small pig's tail. It was the root. The other end was pale green. Mike could see that it was going to make the first leaves of the bean. The tiny plant was fastened to the two large halves of the bean. These two halves were full of food. This is the way a bean is put together. Other seeds are put together in very much the same way.

It had rained the very day Mike's beans were planted, and that was a good thing. The seed could not have started to grow without rain. The water had seeped into the seed through a small opening in the seed coat. Mike could see this opening with his magnifying glass.

Water makes a wonderful thing happen when it gets inside a seed. The seed begins to swell up. The water

IF YOU PUT SOME
SUGAR IN A GLASS
OF WATER

YOU CAN
TASTE IT

THE SUGAR WILL
GO ALL THROUGH
THE WATER

BUT YOU CAN'T
SEE IT

begins to dissolve some of the food that's in the seed. The same thing happens that happens when you put sugar into water. The sugar goes right into the water and everywhere the water goes the sugar goes too. You can taste the sugar in the water but you can't see it. You cannot see the food in the bean when it is dissolved in the water either. Mike couldn't see it with his magnifying glass no matter how hard he looked. But when the food is in the water it goes wherever the water goes.

The tiny bean plant lay next to the food. It was fastened to it. The water dissolved some of the food and carried it into the bean plant. This is why rain is so important to seeds. Lots of people don't know this.

A few days later Mike wanted to have another look at his bean seeds. So he dug one up and looked at it with his magnifying glass. The tiny plant in the seed was bigger than the plant Mike had seen a few days before. The leaves were larger and had begun to push up. The roots were longer and had begun to push down. The bean halves were smaller because the bean plant was using up the food.

The beans were really growing!

One day Mike got a big surprise when he went out to the garden. He ran to the house calling, "Jiminy crickets, the beans are up! Come and see them."

And the beans were up. The two bean halves had grown right up out of the ground.

That is the way with bean seeds. There's nothing unusual about it. Many people think it's very interesting the way beans push themselves up out of the ground when they begin to grow.

The beans pushed farther up into the spring sunlight. Soon Mike could see the row of bean plants from the back porch. The bean halves grew smaller until the food was all used up.

Of course this couldn't have happened to the seeds
if rain hadn't fallen and seeped down into the ground.

But it *did* rain, and all kinds of things happened on
Showers Farm. Mr. McBlossom's corn was up. Before
long every crow in the neighborhood knew that the
corn was up. The wheat was up too. And peas and
peppers and parsley and parsnips were all coming up
in the garden.

Mike's garden was beginning to look like a good
garden looks in spring when it rains and the sun shines.

WATER FOR PLANTS

Mike worked almost every day in his garden. He pulled weeds. He used a hoe to make the ground loose so the rain could sink in. April wasn't much help. But he liked to be with Mike. He usually was.

Mike had some cabbage plants to put in his garden. "You'll never know I've moved you," he said to his cabbages. "I'll plant you so carefully you'll think you are still in that box." Boys like Mike talk to almost anything that's handy if there are no people around. Mr. McBlossom was back in the cornfield. Mrs. McBlossom was working in the house.

Mike lifted the plants and tucked them in the ground. He pressed the earth around the roots. Just as he was planting the last one his LIKING FOR LOOKING got hold of him. "I wonder what those roots would look like under my magnifying glass," he thought.

Instead of planting it, he washed the soil from the roots in a pail of water so he could see the roots better. He saw that the main root branched into smaller ones. These branched into smaller ones and these into smaller ones until the roots were so small they were hard to see. "I wonder if there are still smaller ones," Mike thought. He held his magnifying glass over the roots and looked carefully. Yes, there were smaller ones. There were some as small as hairs.

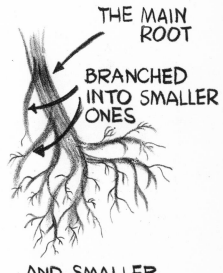

THE MAIN ROOT

BRANCHED INTO SMALLER ONES

AND SMALLER AND SMALLER

These small root hairs were the water-getters for the cabbage plants. The roots of peppers and parsley and peas and parsnips have root hairs too. All garden plants have them. So do trees and other plants. If they didn't they couldn't drink in the rain that falls on the soil where they grow.

All over Mike's garden millions and trillions of root hairs were taking in water. But it wasn't just water that was going into these root hairs. The ground is full of food that plants need to grow. The water dissolves this food. Wherever the water goes the food

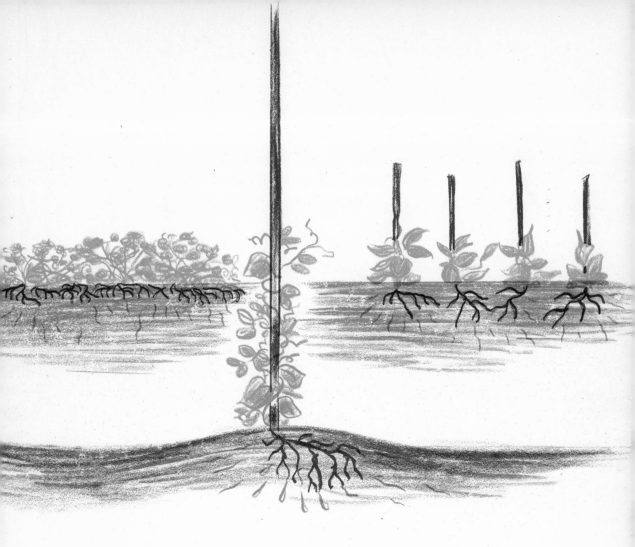

goes too. So when the water went into the root hairs the food went too, and that was a good thing because plants can't grow without it. And if plants didn't grow, where would we get peas and peanuts and pickles and popcorn? And if trees didn't grow, where would we get lumber for handles and houses and bats and barns?

When Mike finished looking at the roots of the cabbage plant he planted it. "Now you can begin to grow," he said. "I'll be watching you."

RAIN IN THE WOODS

The garden and fields were not the only places where rain was important. Across the meadow in the woods where the pond was, the rain in the spring seemed to bring all kinds of things to life.

"Let's walk to the woods and see spring," Mrs. McBlossom said to Mike one day.

"Let's take April," said Mike.

And so Mrs. McBlossom and Mike McBlossom and April McBlossom set out to see spring in the woods.

They looked under the brown leaves and saw tiny points of green coming up out of the black earth. "Seeds are sprouting," said Mrs. McBlossom.

"What kind?" asked Mike.

"Oh, all kinds," said his mother.

And she was right. There were all kinds of seeds sprouting in the woods. Water was seeping into acorn seeds. The acorns were swelling up, popping open, and sending roots down and leaves up. Wild-flower seeds were sprouting too.

Moss that had been brown all winter was getting green. Its roots were bringing in water and food from the soil. Mike and his mother saw tiny ferns beginning to unwrap. The ferns were as fuzzy as kittens' ears. Each day they pushed up through the brown leaves a little farther. Slowly they were unwrapping and spreading out in the spring sunshine. Down in the black soil their roots were taking in water.

They saw trillium and jack-in-the-pulpit flowers begin to push themselves up through the brown leaves. They found violets already in blossom. And they saw the flowers of bloodroot standing up straight and white.

April frightened a rabbit that had been sitting quietly near a log and chased him through the woods, over the seeds that were sprouting, over the moss that was turning green, past the ferns that were unwrapping themselves, past the trilliums and jack-in-the-pulpits and bloodroot, and away.

"Here, April!" called Mrs. McBlossom.

"Come back," called Mike.

"Listen," said Mrs. McBlossom, "I hear something."

She heard the wind flipping through the branches of the trees.

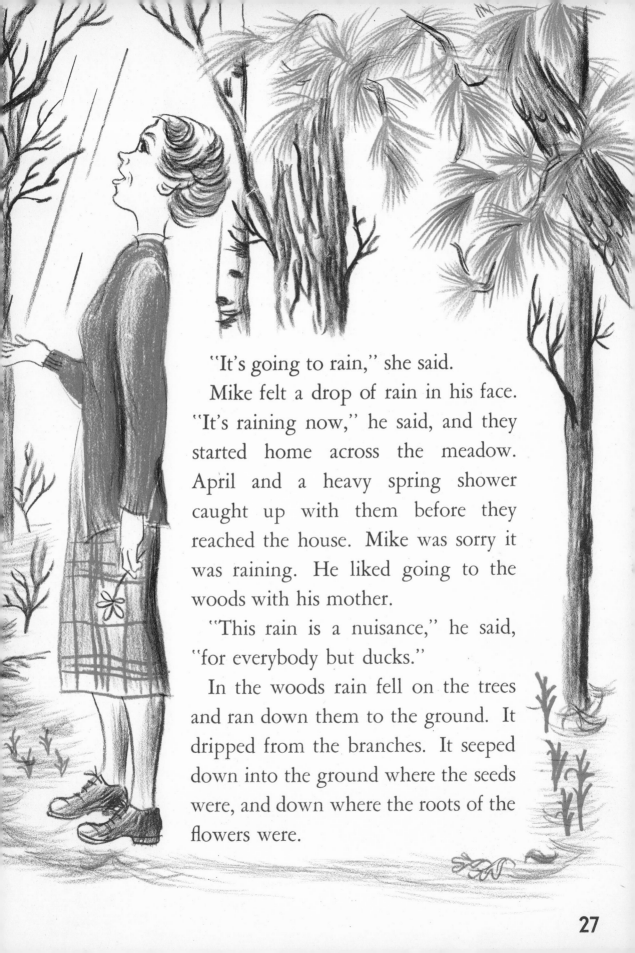

"It's going to rain," she said.

Mike felt a drop of rain in his face. "It's raining now," he said, and they started home across the meadow. April and a heavy spring shower caught up with them before they reached the house. Mike was sorry it was raining. He liked going to the woods with his mother.

"This rain is a nuisance," he said, "for everybody but ducks."

In the woods rain fell on the trees and ran down them to the ground. It dripped from the branches. It seeped down into the ground where the seeds were, and down where the roots of the flowers were.

A POND IN SPRING

One day Mike said to April, "Let's go to the woods. I want to look around and you can chase things and sniff some." Off they went.

At the edge of the woods Mike and April came to a spring pond. In late summer the pond was sometimes very small. But when the spring rains came it grew larger and larger. Rain dripped from leaves of the trees into it. Rain slid down the tree trunks into it. Rain ran into it from all around.

April ran toward the pond, sniffing the ground. Flop! Into the pond jumped a large green frog. Splash! Into the pond leaped a big bullfrog. Blub! Into the pond jumped a big brown toad.

What fun for April to run along the edge of the pond frightening the green frogs and the bullfrogs and the big brown toads. And fun for the frogs and toads that pushed their long legs against the water and swam to where it was deep and quiet.

The deep quiet pond was a wonderful place for animals. A few turtles found it. Snails crept into it. A snake or two wiggled into it. And even a few fish lived there. It was a wonderful place for ducks to swim.

April stood on the bank and watched the splashing water. "You'd like to catch 'em, wouldn't you?" said Mike. "But they're too quick for you. They're slippery too."

The big pond that the spring rains made was a wonderful home for frogs and toads. They had been buried in the mud all winter. When spring came they dug themselves out. Frogs and toads from here and there came to the spring pool. These green and brown jumpers came to the pond in the woods for a very special reason. They didn't come just to sit on the bank and snap flies. They didn't come just to swim and croak. They came to lay their eggs.

The toads laid their eggs in the pond in long strings. The frogs laid theirs in the pond in bunches. After their eggs were laid they kept on croaking and swimming about and sitting on the banks of the pond as if nothing had happened.

FROGS LAY THEIR
EGGS IN BUNCHES

TOADS LAY THEIR EGGS
IN LONG STRINGS

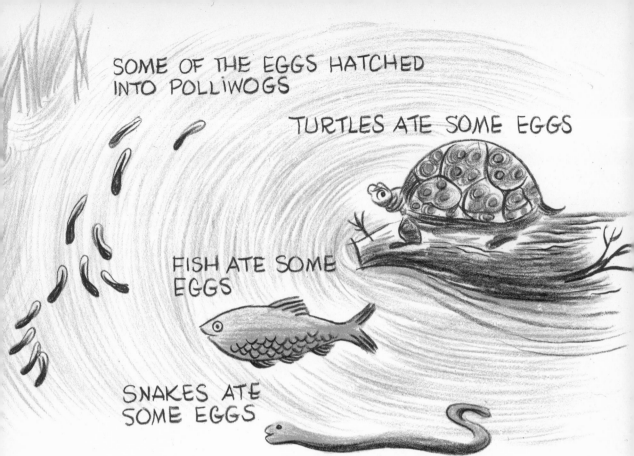

SOME OF THE EGGS HATCHED
INTO POLLIWOGS

TURTLES ATE SOME EGGS

FISH ATE SOME
EGGS

SNAKES ATE
SOME EGGS

They paid no attention to their eggs. They didn't even know the day their eggs hatched into polliwogs. They didn't even know their own polliwogs if they passed them in the pond. They just laid lots of eggs and went on their way. The turtles in the pond would eat some. Snakes might gobble up a few. Fish would snap some up.

But the frogs just laid plenty of eggs and then went about their business of eating insects, swimming in the pond, sitting in the sun, and keeping out of the way of nosy dogs like April.

As far as anyone knows, frogs and toads have always behaved like that.

"There must be frogs' eggs in here," said Mike to April. "I'm going to get some and have a look." He looked into the water but he couldn't see any eggs. He walked around the pond where the sun was bright, and there floating in the water lay a bunch as large as a big fist. He found a can and scooped them up with water from the pond.

"Let's put them in a big glass jar," his mother said when he brought the frogs' eggs to the house. "Then we can see them better."

At first, when Mike looked at them with his magnifying glass, they looked black and were about the size of a BB shot. Each day he watched them. They soon began to change shape. They changed slowly until Mrs. Mc-Blossom said they looked the same shape as grains of rice. And they did.

A few days later Mike was watching them with his magnifying glass and he got the surprise of his life. One of them wiggled. Then another wiggled. He called Mrs. McBlossom. She called Mr. McBlossom, who came running in from the barn with April at his heels. They all watched and saw the little black objects wiggle and twist and jerk, and before long they were swimming around in the glass jar as though they had always been good swimmers.

FIRST THEY LOOKED LIKE BB SHOT

THEN THEY LOOKED LIKE GRAINS OF RICE

"Never saw a thing like that before," said Mr. McBlossom.

"Neither did I," said Mrs. McBlossom.

"I guess it happens all the time," said Mike.

And down in the pond in the woods hundreds of eggs were hatching into polliwogs, which are also called tadpoles. It happened every spring when rain made the pond big.

AND THEN THEY WERE TADPOLES!

A SMALL TADPOLE

1.

2.

3.

4.

FINALLY CHANGED INTO A FROG

5.

The tadpoles would grow and grow. Soon they would have hind legs, then front legs. Then their tails would get shorter. Their bodies would begin to look more like frogs than tadpoles. They would grow larger until finally they would have hardly any tails at all. They changed so that they could breathe on land instead of in water.

And finally they began to hop up on the bank of the pond and blink in the sunshine and snap at insects. And if April came along they plopped into the pond and pushed their legs against the water and swam to where it was deep and quiet.

But this wasn't all that happened in the pond that the rain made. Hundreds and hundreds of other tiny animals lived in the pond. Nobody in the neighborhood ever saw them. They were too small to be noticed, but the pond was a good home for them.

Big snails crawled into the pond that the rain made. They laid eggs that hatched into little snails that grew into big snails that laid eggs and hatched into little snails.

Crayfish dug themselves out of the mud in the woods in spring and crept into the pond. Crayfish look a little like lobsters. They act a little like lobsters too, but they are much smaller. They can swim backward like a streak of lightning. Crayfish laid eggs, and before long there were lots of little crayfish swimming around. They were the color of the brown leaves that lay in the bottom of the pond. You could look right at them and never see them unless they moved.

And even that wasn't all that happened. This is just a small part of the story of the pond on Showers Farm in the spring. But you can see that it's a good thing it rains, especially in the spring. If it didn't, where would frogs and toads and snails and crayfish and all the other animals lay their eggs and raise their families? But it does rain, and that's a good thing.

NO RAIN

Spring came and went. And then it was summer on Showers Farm. And this was a summer everyone on the farm still remembers. People in the city still remember it too. People still talk about it. Even Mike still remembers it.

The sun climbed higher and higher in the sky as it always does in summer. At noon it was straight overhead. It stayed up a long time. The summer days were long. They always are. But this summer was hotter than usual and it didn't rain. It didn't rain for weeks and weeks. Everything on Showers Farm was dry.

All during the spring Mike had wished it wouldn't rain so much. Now he wanted rain very much.

Mike's garden looked sad and so did Mike. The soil was dry. Cabbage plants couldn't grow. Peppers and parsley and peas and parsnips began to wilt. They didn't grow. They couldn't. There was no water to bring them food from the ground.

"Our gardens are a sight!" said Mrs. McBlossom.

Each evening when the sun went down Mike helped her carry water to the gardens. But it was hard to pump and hard to carry. And the garden was big. Mike got very tired. How he wished it would rain! So did everyone else.

When Mike and April went to the pond in the woods they found that it was getting smaller and smaller. Water slowly disappeared from it. It went into the air where it couldn't be seen. The water evaporated into the air. Water does that, especially when days are hot and dry.

The pond grew smaller and smaller until there was hardly room enough for six ducks to sit on it. The tadpoles had hardly room enough to swim without bumping into each other. Some of them died. Some of the other animals in the pond did too.

April couldn't find a frog or a toad to frighten. They had dug down into the ground in the woods. They dug down into the moist ground. They hardly moved at all. Snails dug down into the ground too. So did the turtles and the crayfish.

The earth under the trees in the woods began to dry out. Water evaporated from it into the air. The ferns curled up and began to turn brown. The forest plants were thirsty for water. There was plenty of food in the forest soil but the plants couldn't use it. There was no water to bring it in. There was no rain.

The soil in the farm fields was dry and dusty. When Mr. McBlossom drove the cultivator through the rows of corn a cloud of dust followed after him. The leaves of the corn curled up and some of them turned brown. The hot wind blew into the cornfield. It rattled the brown corn leaves.

The road past the farm was dry and dusty; the grass and bushes along the road were dry and dusty. The grass looked brown and dead. The fields in the meadow were brown. The cows were hungry. They were thirsty too, for the creek that ran down through the fields and meadows was almost dry.

"If it doesn't rain soon, it will be too late," said Mr. McBlossom. "Our corn and clover will be dead. We shall have to sell the cows and pigs."

"There won't be any vegetables to sell," said Mrs. McBlossom.

April spent most of the day lying under the porch trying to keep cool. The days were too hot and dry even for Mike to fly his kite or do anything else that he liked to do.

Mike wished that it would rain.

But there was not a cloud to be seen.

Down the lane, up the road, past the church, and over the bridge in the city, people looked at the sky for signs of rain.

In the city it was hot. The grass and trees needed water. There was not enough water in the reservoir. The people were careful not to waste water. There was hardly enough water to use for all the things city people use water for.

And it didn't rain and it didn't rain.

SHOWERS TOMORROW

Then one day the weather report said *Possible showers*. The next day the report said *Showers tomorrow*, and people watched the sky for signs of rain.

But the next day there wasn't a cloud in sight.

But the next day after that Mike saw a few puffs of white clouds riding in the blue sky.

"Looks as if it's going to rain!" he cried, and Mrs. McBlossom and Farmer McBlossom came running out of the house to look up.

They watched the clouds. Soon the puffs got a little larger and then a little longer. They were white like the cloud that comes out of a teakettle sitting on a very hot stove. They were made of the same thing. They were made of very, very tiny droplets of water smaller than the period at the end of this sentence. But there were a great many of them. The puffs of clouds in the blue sky were made of more tiny droplets of water than you could ever count if you were the best counter in town and lived to be a hundred. The water that had evaporated in the air was beginning to come out again. Water comes out of the air if it is cooled enough. And the air up high was getting cooler.

The clouds got larger and larger and darker and darker. Soon they covered the blue in the sky and the day got quite dark. People watched the sky and waited for the rain to fall. Especially the people on Showers Farm.

AT FIRST THE CLOUDS WERE MADE OF TINY DROPLETS

WHICH FINALLY GOT SO LARGE AND HEAVY

THAT THEY COULD NOT FLOAT ON THE AIR ANY LONGER

SO DOWN THEY FELL

The tiny droplets in the clouds grew larger. The air got cooler. Then the droplets got so large that they were too heavy to stay floating in the air. They began to fall down and down toward the earth. At first only a few drops hit the earth. It was sprinkling. Then more and more fell. It was raining. It rained on the city and it rained on the country.

Mrs. McBlossom stood at her kitchen window and watched the rain fall. Mr. McBlossom stood in his barn door watching the rain fall. Anyone could tell that they were glad.

But Mike didn't watch the rain from the window of his room. He put on his raincoat and his rain hat and went outdoors. April went with him.

"Let's go look at the garden," he said. And so they did. Mike watched the rain fall on the peppers and the parsley and the peas and parsnips. It made them green and fresh. It slipped and dripped off to the ground. It soaked down into the ground and the roots began to fill up. "It's a good thing it's raining," thought Mike. "It's no nuisance today. It's plenty necessary."

Back in the woods the rain made the pond get bigger again. Toads and frogs hopped out from where they had been hiding. They jumped around in the wet grass and on the wet moss and hopped into the pond and out of it. Snails stuck out their feelers and looked about. The tadpoles wagged their tails in the water and there was plenty of room, for the pond was getting larger. Ducks waddled to the pond and slid into the water and quacked and swam.

The earth in the forest soaked up the water and the plants began to drink it. The dry earth in the cornfield soaked up the water and the corn plants drank it. Along the roadside the grass and trees and bushes got a bath and their roots reached out for the water.

Down the lane, up the road, past the church, and over the bridge the cool rain was washing the city. It ran down the pavement over the sidewalks and washed everything the way rain does. It ran down the mountainside into the city reservoir and began to fill it up. People in the city were glad.

Mike was glad too. He watched the rain make a puddle in the dooryard. He built a small dam to make the puddle larger. April helped him.

"April," he said, "it's a good thing it rains—and not only for ducks!"

Even the chickens on Showers Farm seemed to be glad. They didn't run under the hay wagon or into the henpen. They stayed out in the rain and made that funny sound that chickens make. Mike said, "Even the chickens are glad. I think they are singing."

And maybe they were.